MW00817028

TALES OF THE Destroyer

"COOKING LESSON"

story & art
by

M. RASHEED

Based on characters created by
WARREN MURPHY & RICHARD SAPIR

Second Sight Graphix
7413 Six Forks Rd, Suite #207
Raleigh, NC 27615
www.mrasheed.com

story & art by

M. RASHEED

ISBN: 978-09915266-0-4
Story and artwork © copyright co-owned by M. Rasheed (author/artist) and Warren Murphy.
Printed in the United States of America by www.lightningsource.com
Library of Congress Control Number: 2014900625
No part of this book may be produced or used in any form or by any means-graphic, electronic, mechanical, including photocopying, recording, taping, or information storage and retrieval systems-without written permission of the author.
All characters depicted within these pages, including those of Remo Williams, The Destroyer, Masters of Sinanju, Chiun, Dr. Harold W. Smith, CURE, and Folcroft Sanitarium are owned by Warren Murphy.

Additional information about The Destroyer novel series, comics, and/or characters can be found at the websites below:

https://destroyerbooks.com/
http://www.sinanju.net/
https://www.facebook.com/destroyerbooks
http://www.mrasheed.com

CURE. This agency of the United States government is so secret it is only known by three people. The reason it is so secret is enormous: The agency is designed to work outside of the Constitution in order to keep the country working smoothly...fairly...justly... the way it was intended. CURE's very existence is an admission that the American Experiment doesn't work. The leakage of its existence would be a great embarrassment to the American people, making them a laughing stock in the world's eyes. So other than the President of the United States himself, only CURE's director Harold Smith and the enforcement arm code-named *"The Destroyer"* make up the agency. With the extraordinary task of secretly running the entire country, each of these men must necessarily be extraordinary. Dr. Smith is the most patriotic, loyal, frugal, perfectionistic, researcher and administrator in the world. A past president chose him to run CURE because he knew no one would be more qualified to administrate a country-wide organization all by himself, a task he assumed would only last for a decade or so. And when the president came to the difficult decision that the secret agency needed an enforcement arm for those bad seeds who couldn't be rehabilitated, Smith knew that only a man as special as himself would do.

The House of Sinanju. A five-thousand-year-old tradition of super assassins originating in a small, unassuming fishing village in North Korea. A single master passing the deadly art of the same name on to only one pupil at a time, Sinanju's practitioners have hired themselves out to history's kings, pharoahs, sultans, and emperors, and single-handedly controlled the course of human destiny for ages. But now the current Master of Sinanju is offered a new task: to train an American secret agent to join his exclusive tradition of men so deadly, that no human on earth can survive once they've marked you as a target.

He is hired to train a *Destroyer.*

THERE HE IS!
SH!

MARK IS SO **WEIRD**.
LOOK AT HIS PANTS!

GIGGLE!
HEY, MARKY!
SH!

SIGH!
WHY IS HE MAKING THAT NOISE?
MAYBE HE HAS ASTHMA.
MAYBE HE'S **STUPID**.

SUCK YOUR INHALER, FAGGOT!
SH!
TAK!

GIGGLE
GIGGLE
OKAY, LEAVE HIM ALONE BEFORE HE CRIES OR SOMETHING.

OH MY **GOD**! THAT WOULD BE HILARIOUS!
SH! HERE'S MR. DAWSON...

DON'T, TONY!
WHAT?

I'M JUST HAVING A LITTLE FUN.
TAK!
THE NIHILIST RECIPES

WHO THREW THAT?
TONY!
THE NIHILIST RECIPES

THAT WILL BE **ENOUGH**, YOUNG MAN.
A'IGHT.
THE NIHILIST RECIPES

CLASS, GO TO CHAPTER 17 IN YOUR TEXTS.
THE NIHILIST RECIPES

MR. SIMMONS, PUT YOUR BOOK AWAY AND PULL OUT YOUR TEXT.

DID YOU HEAR ME?

MARK!

THANK YOU.
NOW IF YOU WOULD BE SO KIND AS TO **JOIN** US?
DUMB ASS.
GIGGLE

RICHLAND
RICHLAND HIGH SCHOOL

hi.
W-WHAT?

HI.
HELLO.

i'd like to see you... uh... when... uh... do... i mean... uh...

UH UH!
LISTEN, I HAVE TO GET TO CLASS.
NOW.
GOOD TALKING TO YOU.
OR WHAT-EVER.

THE NIHILIST RECIPES

THERE HE IS!
SH!

BAM!
NO!

AAAAA!!
BAM
BAM
BAM
BAM
BAM
BAM
BAM

GUH!
BAM
BAM
BAM
BAM

BAM
BAM
BAM
BAM

BAM
BAM
BAM

BAM
BAM
BAM

HIS NAME WAS REMO...
...AND HE COULD ONLY KILL WITH ONE FINGER.
WHO IS IT?
ERWIN RABINOWITZ?
OPEN UP.
IT'S ME.
109
"COOKING LESSON" STORY AND ART BY M. RASHEED
BASED ON CHARACTERS CREATED BY WARREN MURPHY AND RICHARD SAPIR

"ME?"
WHO IS "ME?"
MORGAN SENT ME.

AH!
WELL, WHY DIDN'T YOU SAY SO?
WHERE IS SHE?
109

I LEFT HER OVER IN APARTMENT 124...
...WITH THE REST OF THEM.

WHAT?! WHAT'D YOU GO AND DO SOMETHING LIKE THAT FOR?! THAT BLOOMBERG IS EVEN GREEDIER THAN I AM!

THERE'S NO WAY SHE'S STILL A VIRGIN NOW! ARE YOU SHITTIN' ME?!

THERE'S NO WAY I'M PAYIN' FOR THAT!

OH, YOU'LL PAY ALRIGHT.
REMO'S MUSCLES FLEX...

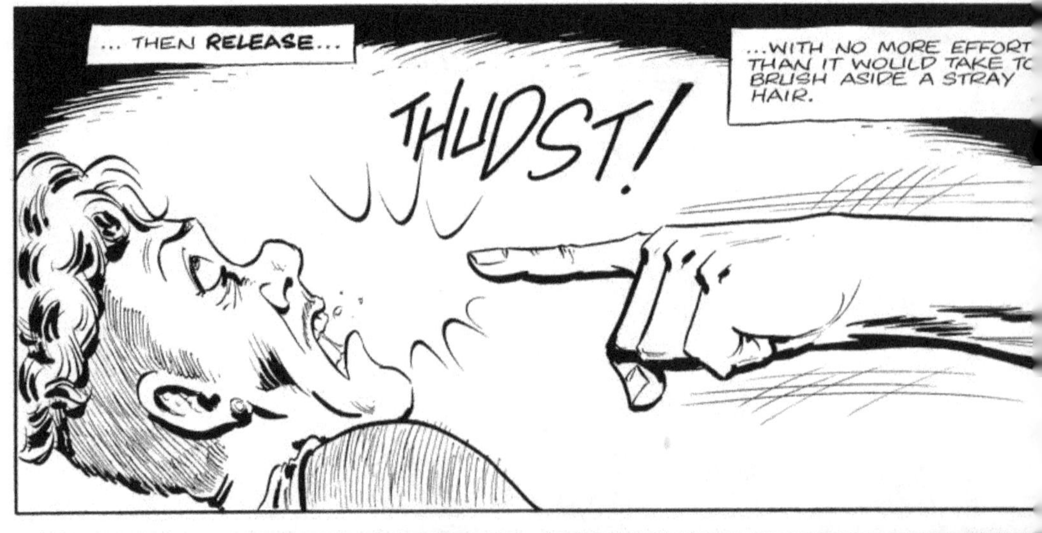
... THEN RELEASE...
...WITH NO MORE EFFORT THAN IT WOULD TAKE TO BRUSH ASIDE A STRAY HAIR.
THUDST!

AND YET THE IMPACT OF HIS INDEX FINGER HAS COMPLETELY PULVERIZED ERWIN RABINOWITZ'S SKULL...

...HIS NOW-SHAPELESS HEAD LYING ON HIS CARPET LIKE A POORLY-STUFFED BEANBAG.

NEXT.
APARTMENT 124.
109
CLK!

REMO IS A MASTER OF SINANJU, THE AGES-OLD ART OF THE ASSASSIN.
AND FOR THE TENANTS OF THE THEODORE MORGAN APARTMENTS, HE'S DEATH HIMSELF.

NOK NOK
NOK

YEAH?
WHERE'S BLOOMBERG?
MORGAN SENT ME.

BOSS?

YOU FROM MORGAN?
YUP.

WELL, YOU WILL TELL HIM THAT SIX YEARS OLD IS TOO OLD. TOO MUCH ATTITUDE.

IS THAT RIGHT.
YES.
I WANT THEM TO ADORE ME.

YOU WILL TELL MORGAN THAT I WANT NOTHING OLDER THAN THREE.
OR ELSE MY LAWYER WILL LEARN THAT MY TIME IN HIS HALFWAY HOUSE WAS LESS THAN SATISFACTORY.

YOU KNOW WHAT? THAT WILL ACTUALLY BE KIND OF DIFFICULT FOR ME CONSIDERING MORGAN IS DEAD.
WHAT?!

WHAT HAPPENED TO HIM?
THIS HAPPENED:

STOOSH!

SOME MARTIAL ARTS ARE FAMOU
FOR ENABLING THE STUDENT
TO USE HIS OWN ENERGY
EFFICIENTLY.

124

LIKE KARATE.
ITS PRACTITIONERS FOCUS ALL OF THEIR POWER INTO ONE DEADLY STRIKE.
KIYAH!!

BUT SINANJU, THE SUN SOURCE OF ALL THE MARTIAL DISCIPLINES...
POK!
UG!

...GENERATES ITS OWN ENERGY.
BRAKKA!

PASH!
DAMN.

SPAK!
ERG!

THUS MASTERS OF SINANJU CAN ROUTINELY PERFORM FANTASTIC FEATS...

...WITHOUT USING ANY OF THEIR OWN BODIES' POWER AND STRENGTH...
PUHP!

..MAKING ALL MOVEMENTS SEEM COMPLETELY EFFORTLESS.

P-PLEASE...!
WHERE'RE THE CHILDREN?
IN THERE!

THANKS.
KRAK!

"C'MON, KIDS."
"LET'S GET YOU HOME."

COLUMBI
HIGH SCH
CLASS OF

LOOK AT THAT FAT FUCK HOLLISTER.
AW, LEAVE HIM ALONE, DANNY.

WHATEVER.
I WISH HE'D DROP OUT OR SOMETHING.
fuck you.

HI.
HI.

I HEARD WHAT THAT ASSHOLE SAID ABOUT YOU.
I WANT YOU TO KNOW THAT GUYS LIKE US...

...WE DON'T HAVE TO BE ALONE ANYMORE.
W-WHAT ?

HAVE YOU EVER HEARD OF ROBERT POWERS?

HE WROTE THAT **BOOK**, RIGHT?
ABOUT HOW TO BLOW UP PEOPLE'S CARS AND STUFF?

THANKS BUT I'M **NOT** TRYING TO JOIN THE SKINHEADS OR ANYTHING.
IT'S NOT **THAT** SERIOUS.

DO I **LOOK** LIKE A SKINHEAD, DUDE?

LISTEN, THIS IS ABOUT FAIRNESS AND CHANGE...

...AND FINALLY GETTING **OUR** SHARE.
THAT'S **IT**.

ALL I'M ASKING IS FOR YOU TO COME HEAR THE MESSAGE FOR YOURSELF.
BUT IF YOU **PREFER** TO HAVE POPULAR PRICKS ALWAYS FUCKING WITH YOU ALL THE TIME--!

OKAY! **ALRIGHT** ALREADY.
EXCELLENT!
I'LL PICK YOU UP AT SIX!

STARING INTENSELY AT THE COMPUTER HIDDEN WITHIN HIS DESK, DR. HAROLD W. SMITH IS IN A UNIQUE POSITION.

TAK TAK TAK TAK TAK TAK TAK

HAND-PICKED IN THE EARLY '60 BY A YOUNG PRESIDENT, DR. SMITH WAS CHOSEN AS MUCH FOR HIS PENNY-PINCHING FRUGALITY...

HE MOST POWERFUL COMPUTER
YSTEM MONEY CAN BUY SETS TO
VORK PROCESSING TRILLIONS UPON
TRILLIONS OF BYTES IN AN INSTANT
VITH THE TAP OF A KEY.

THE SHOOTINGS CORRELATE TO THE DATES OF ROBERT POWERS' BOOK TOUR.

THIS IS CHIUN, THE REIGNING GUARDIAN OF THE NORTH KOREAN FISHING VILLAGE OF SINANJU.
AND, LIKE HIS STUDENT, REMO, CHIUN IS A MASTER OF THE MARTIAL ART OF THE SAME NAME.

ALSO LIKE REMO, CHIUN'S MASTERY OF SINANJU GRANTS HIM PHENOMENAL ABILITIES THAT MANY WOULD TERM **SUPER-HUMAN**.

SUCH AS HIS SENSE OF HEARING, FOR EXAMPLE. CHIUN CAN DETECT A HUMAN HEARTBEAT AT A THOUSAND YARDS AWAY.
22134

HE CAN EVEN DISTINGUISH BETWEEN VARIOUS PEOPLE BY THE MINUTE DIFFERENCES IN EACH BEAT.

SO DESPITE REMO'S EQUALLY SUPER-HUMAN ABILITY TO MOVE AS QUIETLY AS A FALLING HAIR...

SO YOU FAILED TO CARRY OUT MY INSTRUCTION.
...HE COULD **NEVER** SNEAK PASS CHIUN.
D'OH!

GIVE ME A BREAK.
HOW COULD YOU **KNOW** THAT?

HOW LONG HAVE I BEEN YOUR TEACHER?
ABOUT... WHAT? ALMOST TWENTY YEARS NOW?

IN TWENTY YEARS I SHOULD NOT KNOW MY STUDENT?

DESPITE THE EMPEROR SMITH'S SELFISH ATTEMPTS TO BIND THE HOUSE TO THE BARBARIC WEST...

... I HAVE **NOT** BECOME AMERICANIZED.
TELL ME ABOUT IT.

I AM STILL **KOREAN**. AS SUCH I'VE RETAINED MY BASIC POWERS OF OBSERVATION THAT YOU LOWLY WESTERNERS HAVE OBVIOUSLY **FAILED** TO CULTIVATE.

INSIDE OF MY VERY **FIRST** YEAR OF INSTRUCTING YOU IN THE GLORIOUS ART OF SINANJU, THE PERFECT SUN SOURCE OF ALL THE ARTS, THE FLOWER OF PE--!
CAN WE GET TO THE POINT, PLEASE?

SIP

MY **POINT** IS THAT IT DIDN'T TAKE LONG TO NOTICE YOUR HOLLOW, ARROGANT BLUSTER.

IF YOU **HAD** PASSED THE TEST, YOU WOULD HAVE PRACTICALLY KICKED THE DOOR IN...

...JUMPING UP AND DOWN AROUND MY KIMONO HEM LIKE A PUPPY TO **BOAST** OF YOUR MEAGER ACCOMPLISHMENT.

BUT **INSTEAD** YOU CONSPICUOUSLY DIDN'T WANT ME TO KNOW HOW YOU FAIRED.
YOUR SILENCE, REMO WILLIAMS, SPOKE **VOLUMES**.

PERHAPS YOUR **NEXT** LESSON WILL BE ONE TO GRANT **YOU** OBSERVATION.
HEY!
I'M **GREAT** AT OBSERVING. I **WAS** A PRETTY GOOD COP, AFTER ALL.

"PRETTY GOOD?"
YOU'RE **BARELY** AN ADEQUATE ASSASSIN.
AS A "PRETTY GOOD" COP YOU WERE ARRESTED AND EXECUTED, REMEMBER?

I WAS FRAMED AND YOU **KNOW** IT!
AH.
AN EXCUSE.
TYPICAL FOR AN AMERICAN.

AND WHAT WAS YOUR EXCUSE FOR USING ANYTHING EXCEPT THE ONE FINGER PER MY INSTRUCTION?

WELL?

I **HATE** YOU.
THAT WILL BE THE EMPEROR SMITH.
I **KNOW.**

TELL HIM THAT I REQUIRE MORE GOLD TO TRAIN A LOWLY "PRETTY GOOD" ASSASSIN, TO COMPENSATE FOR THE ADDED STRESS.

NOW WHAT?!
R-REMO?

YEAH?
IT DIDN'T EVEN RING! PERHAPS THERE'S A BREACH?--

RELAX, SMITTY. IT'S FINE. I DIDN'T WANT IT TO RING.
WHAT DO YOU WANT?

OH.
WELL, AHEM!
REMO, I HAVE A MISSION OF GREAT IMPORTANCE!

SO WHAT'S NEW? THERE'S ALWAYS SOME MATTER OF GREAT IMPORTANCE EVER SINCE YOU FIRST FRAMED ME.

YOU WERE RECRUITED FOR SERVICE TO YOUR COUNTRY.
THE "FRAME" WAS JUST A COVER.

HAT AM I STUPID THAT I DON'T KNOW THE
IFFERENCE BETWEEN FRAMED AND RECRUITED?
 WAS A COP, AND A VIETNAM VET, FOR
HRISSAKE!
YOU RUINED MY LIFE!

REMO, LISTEN TO ME:
YOU LOVE THIS COUNTRY AS MUCH AS I DO. BUT IT HAS FLAWS.
FLAWS THAT ENABLE DISEASE-MINDED SCUM TO DISMANTLE THE NATION USING THE VERY HIGH-MINDED IDEALS THAT MAKE THIS COUNTRY GREAT.

THIS ORGANIZATION...
...COMPOSED OF THE TWO OF US AND THE PRESIDENT...
...IS THE ONLY CURE AGAINST THOSE DISEASED MINDS.

WITHOUT EACH OF US DOING OUR PART, THE WHOLE COUNTRY WILL COLLAPSE.
DO YOU WANT THAT?

NO.
THEN PLEASE STAY FOCUSED.
PLEASE.

I NEED YOU TO INVESTIGATE A CONTROVERSIAL BOOK AUTHOR.
HE MAY BE UP TO NO GOOD."
I CAN'T BELIEVE HOW GOOD THAT WAS!
I KNOW! HE MADE TOTAL SENSE!
THE NIHILIST RECIPES
THE NIHILIST RECIPES

THANKS, DUDE.
HEY, NO PROB. LIKE MR. POWERS SAID, "I WANT YOU TO GET YOURS."

HI, MR. POWERS, SIR!
HELLO. WHO SHOULD I MAKE THIS OUT TO?
THE NIHILIST RECIPES

DERRICK HOLLISTER! YOU AR
AN INSPIRATION, SIR! I GOTTA ADMIT I'VE NEVER HEARD ANYTHING LIKE THAT BEFORE!

OF COURSE YOU HAVEN'T. ONLY THE POPULAR AND ANYONE WILLING TO SUCK UP TO THEM ARE ALLOWED TO BE EMPOWERED.

THAT'S WHY I NEED YOU TO UNDERSTAND THAT THE ONLY WAY YOU'RE GOING TO GET YOUR SHARE IS TO TAKE IT!

YOU HEAR ME?
OH, YES, SIR!
FUCK'EM!

IF YOU'RE TIRED OF BEING RUN OVER, FIGHT! IF YOU'RE TIRED OF COMING IN LAST, FIGHT!
THE NIHILIST RECIPES

NOW YOU TAKE THIS BOOK AND USE THE RECIPES TO MAKE A REAL CHANGE!
THE NIHILIST RECIPES

DIDN'T I **TELL** YOU? **DIDN'T** I?
DUDE, I'M GOING **BACK** TO SIGN UP AS A VOLUNTEER OR SOMETHING!

WHO DO I MAKE THIS OUT TO?
ROBERT POWERS IS A MAN WITH A PURPOSE.

BUT HE DIDN'T ALWAYS HAVE ONE.
OH NO.

ONCE HE WAS JUST A DIRTY PUNK KID TERRIFIED HE'D BE DRAFTED INTO VIETNAM.

HE WAS AFRAID TO DIE. SO HE WROTE A BOOK THAT WAS THE SUM TOTAL OF ALL THE FEAR A 19 YEAR OLD COULD VOMIT.
THE NIHILIST RECIPES
BY ROBERT POWERS

BY ITSELF IT WAS AN AMUSING AND FOOLISH RANT FULL OF POTENTIALLY DANGEROUS SCIENCE EXPERIMENTS.
AUTO BATTER
PLASTIQUE

IN THE HANDS OF THE FEARFUL IT COULD BE A GUIDEBOOK OF FEROCIOUS BRUTALITY.

EVENTUALLY HE GREW UP AND BECAME A PRODUCTIVE MEMBER OF SOCIETY. HE NO LONGER BELIEVED IN VIOLENCE AS A SOLUTION TO ANYTHING, NOT EVEN HIS OWN FEARS.

A UNIVERSITY GRADUATE, HE DECIDED TO DEDICATE HIS LIFE TO UNDOING THE TAINT HIS ADOLESCENT FOLLY RELEASED UPON THE WORLD BY BEING A GUIDE TO THE YOUTH.

IT DIDN'T TAKE LONG FOR HIM TO GROW GENUINELY SOURED OVER HIS HOME NATION'S POLICY OF VIOLENCE IN FOREIGN CLIMES...

...SO ROBERT SPREAD HIS PEACEFUL TEACHING MINISTRIES TO OTHER SHORES.

AFRICA.
ASIA.
PASSPORT
USA
MICHIGAN

THEN EUROPE.
HE WAS OFFERED THE SUPERINTENDENT POSITION AT THE INTERNATIONAL SCHOOL IN MADRID.

HE WAS THRILLED.
HE TRAVELED THERE AT ONCE TO SEAL THE DEAL...
...AND TO SEE THE MAGNIFICENT ANCIENT CITY...

...TO FIND HER...

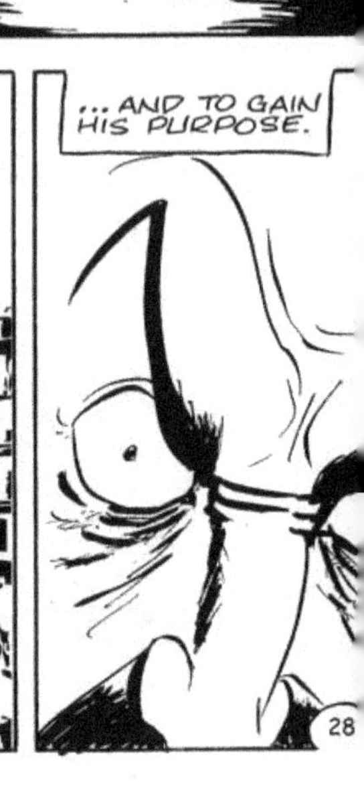
...AND TO GAIN HIS PURPOSE.

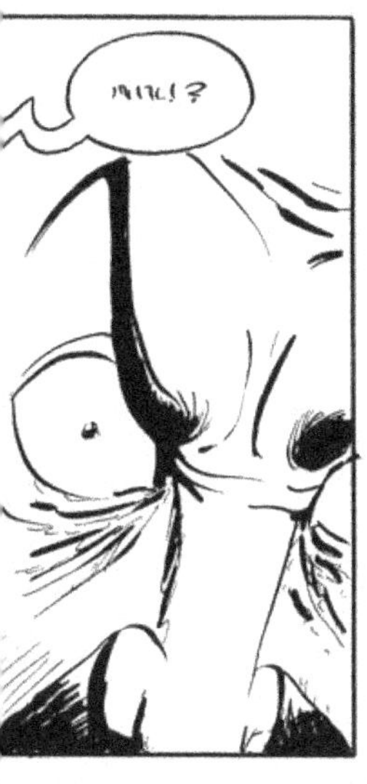
HUH!?

MR. POWERS?

SIR?
MR. POWERS?
YEAH!
YES?

SIR, THERE ARE F.B.I. SPECIAL AGENTS TO SEE YOU.
OH?
THE NIHILIST RECIPES

DENVER INTERNATIONAL AIRPORT.
"I DON'T EVEN UNDERSTAND WHY YOU WANTED TO COME ALONG."

I JUST GOTTA OFF SOME DRAFT DODGER THEN WE'RE **GONE**.

THE EMPEROR SAID IT WAS AN INVESTIGATION.

YOU DON'T KNOW IF THIS DODGER OF DRAFT IS THE ONE YOU SEEK.

LOOK, LET **ME** HANDLE **MY** JOB, HM?
THERE'S ANOTHER ONE.

I REALLY DON'T SEE WHY YOU NEEDED THREE TRUNKS EITHER.

'COURSE YOU AREN'T THE ONE CARRYING THEM.

BUT WE'RE ONLY GOING TO BE HERE A FEW HOURS TOPS.

!

GOD DAMN IT, CHIUN!!
YOU'RE VERY LOUD.

COME ON!!
I'M COMING.
SMITTY IS GOING TO HAVE A SHIT FIT!!

DENVER CIVIC CENTER
I CAN'T BELIEVE YOU.
TAXI

WHAT IS THERE DIFFICULT TO BELIEVE?

SHOULD THE MASTER OF SINANJU ALLOW HIMSELF TO BE MANHANDLED LIKE A RUSSIAN RAPE VICTIM?
HELP YOU?

YEAH, I'M REMOOOOOO...

...TYSON! F.B.I. I NEED TO SPEAK TO ROBERT POWERS IMMEDIATELY.
FBI

COME THIS WAY.
FIRST OF ALL, I DIDN'T SEE ANYBODY "MANHANDLING" YOU.

YOUR NEXT LESSON WILL DEFINITELY BE ONE OF OBSERVATION.
SECOND OF ALL...

...THERE HAD TO BE AT **LEAST** 8 MILLION WAYS TO HANDLE THAT **OTHER** THAN PUBLIC DECAPITATION.
MR. POWERS WILL BE WITH YOU SHORTLY.
THANKS.

WOE THAT ANY FUTURE MASTERS SHOULD BE VICTIMS TO THE DEPTHS OF INGRATITUDE THAT YOU SUBJECT ME TO.
DAILY.

WHAT THE **HELL** DOES YOU TRYING TO COMPROMISE THE SECRECY OF THE ENTIRE ORGANIZATION HAVE TO DO WITH **MY** INGRATITUDE?

THEN YOU ADMIT YOU'RE UNGRATEFUL.
WELL, AT LEAST I'M MAKING **SOME** PROGRESS.

OH, GOOD GRIEF!
NEVER LET IT BE SAID THAT TRAINING A WESTERNER IS **COMPLETELY** FRUITLESS.
AFTER 20 YEARS THEY **MIGHT** EVEN ACHIEVE THE RANK OF "PRETTY GOOD."

AGENT TYSON?
WHAT?!
MR. POWERS WILL SEE YOU NOW.

HELLO, GENTLE...
SPECIAL AGENTS. F.B.I.
...MEN?
I'M REMO.
WHAT IS **THIS**?
THIS IS CHIUN.

HEY... NOW, I'M **VERY** WELL ACQUAINTED WITH THE F.B.I. AND I'VE NEVER SEEN **ANY** OF THEM LOOK LIKE YOU.
OR **THAT**.

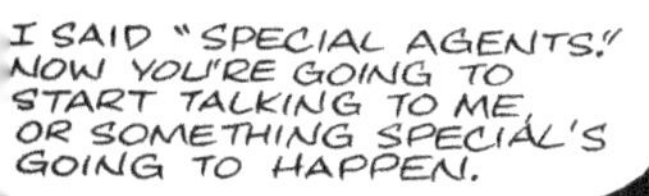
I SAID "SPECIAL AGENTS." NOW YOU'RE GOING TO START TALKING TO ME, OR SOMETHING SPECIAL'S GOING TO HAPPEN.

TO **YOU**.
CAPISCE?

NOW I **KNOW** YOU'RE NOT F.B.I.
WHO **ARE** YOU?

ONE MORE CHANCE: WHAT HAVE YOU BEEN DOING TO THESE KIDS?

HELPING THEM.
HOW? BY TEACHING THEM TO HATE THEIR GOVERNMENT AND KILL INNOCENTS?

OH, THOSE WEREN'T THE INNOCENTS.

THE INNOCENTS ARE THE ONES TIRED OF BEING STEPPED ON AND TREATED LIKE CRAP BY SOCIETY'S FAVORITES.

I'M SHOWING THE INNOCENTS HOW THEY CAN FINALLY GET THEIR DUE.

BY GUNNING DOWN THEIR CLASSMATES.

NO, BY GIVING THEM COURAGE, AND THE FIGHTING SPIRIT OF THE WARRIOR.

SHOWING THEM HOW IT FEELS TO BE THE ALPHA DOG FOR ONCE.

IT'S NOT MY FAULT THAT SOME OF THEM ARE SO DAMAGED BY ABUSE, THEY CAN'T HANDLE WHAT I GIVE THEM.

THAT'S LIKE BLAMING KOOL-AID FOR JIM JONES.

IF WE ARE DONE I'LL NEED YOU TO LEAVE.
I HAVE TO PREPARE FOR TONIGHT'S SEMINAR.
THE

RNNNG!!

YES, REMO?
IT'S **HIM.**
IT'S POWERS.

HE PRACTICALLY **WANTS** ME TO DROP HIS ASS INTO THE VOID.

WHAT?
HE CONFESSED?

WELL... NOT IN SO MANY WORDS.

BUT HE **WAS** BRAGGING ABOUT HOW HE WAS TURNING THEM INTO 'FIGHTING WARRIORS' OR WHATEVER.

LIKE HYPNOSIS?
NNNOOO... I DON'T **THINK** SO...

HE SAYS HE'S **JUST** SHOWING THEM THE WAY TO EMPOWERMENT AND IT'S NOT HIS FAULT IF A FEW LOOSE SCREWS FLY OFF THE HANDLE.

WHEN'S HIS NEXT SHOW?
TONIGHT.
ATTEND THE SHOW AND OBSERVE HIS TECHNIQUE. IF NOTHING DEFINITIVE SHOWS UP...

"...WE'LL JUST HAVE TO LOOK ELSEWHERE."
NOK
NOK
NOK
NOK
COME IN.

HELLO, AGAIN, SIR! IT'S DERRICK! DERRICK **HOLLISTER**!
WELL, **HEY**! WHAT ARE **YOU** DOING HERE?

I'VE JOINED YOUR TOUR CREW AS A VOLUNTEER, SIR!

I ALSO WANTED TO LET YOU KNOW HOW MUCH I APPRECIATE YOUR MESSAGE.
WHAT YOU'RE DOING FOR US LITTLE GUYS.

WELL, YOU'RE **NOT** A LITTLE GUY ANYMORE, RIGHT?
OH **NO**, SIR! I'M A **BIG DOG**!

I'M GLAD TO HEAR IT.
ME TOO, SIR!

AND I PLAN TO MAKE YOU REAL PROUD! YOU'LL SEE!
AND THANK YOU AGAIN!

KLK!

COLUMBINE
HIGH SCHOOL

NOW IT'S **MY** TURN, ASSHOLES.

NO.

SO SHE'S BACK.
WHAT?
WHO ARE YOU?
SHE KNOWS ME.
AND IT'S TIME FOR HER HOLD TO BE BROKEN AGAIN.

MY GODDESS.

ANAT.
TALK TO ME AGAIN.
PLEASE.

LIKE YOU DID IN MADRID.

TELL ME AGAIN THAT YOU LOVE ME.

MY LOVE... MY GODDESS... I'VE ASSEMBLED YOUR ARMY AS YOU'VE ASKED.
THEY AWAIT YOUR COMMAND!

THEY GROW RESTLESS.
TELL THEM WHAT TO DO.

ROOBERRRRRT...
Y-YES!
MYY... LOOOOOOVE...

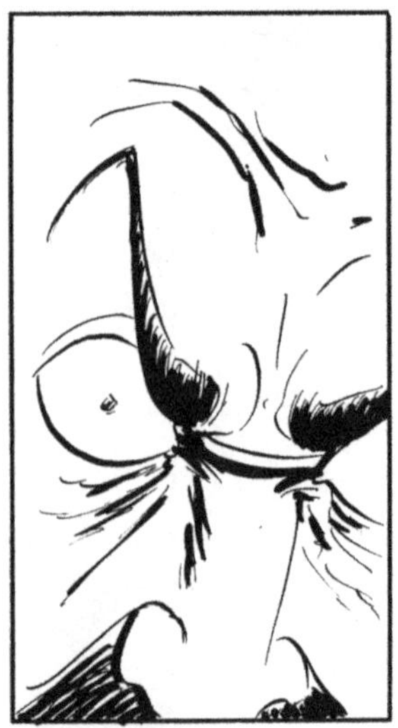

GAH!!

MY GODDESS! SP-SPEAK TO ME!
ROBERRRRT... I NEED YOU...

I MUST BECOME FLESH AGAIN... I MUST LEAD MY ARMY AS IN TIMES OF OLDE...
INSTRUCT ME!

GRRNNHH!
NO!
YESSS...

SACRIFICE FOR ME, ROBERT...
...AGAIN...
NO! MY FAMILY! NO!

I AM YOUR FAMILY NOW...
WHEN I AM FLESH, YOU WILL RIDE AT MY SIDE...
MY GENERAL... ...MY LOVER... ...MY SON...
SOB

MAKE ME FLESH, ROBERT AND ALL YOUR CHILDHOOD DREAMS...
...YOUR TRUE DREAMS...
...WILL BE REAL...
WILL THEY BE REAL?

OH YESSS...
IN THE OLDE DAYS, MY SWORD WAS THE ONLY REALITY...

"EVEN MY BROTHER BA'AL FEARED MY FEROCITY!"

"THE GODS AND HUMANITY ALIKE WERE BUT FODDER FOR MY BLADE..."
...AND THE OLD AND WEAK FOR MY ARROWS...
...AND I KNEW MUCH JOY!

"BUT EVENTUALLY, HUMANITY AND HER DIVINE PATRON GREW STRONG."
"THEY SMOTE MY FLESH..."

"...LEAVING ONLY MY EFFIGIES BEHIND."
"...MY POWER LESSENED."
"ONCE I ATTEMPTED TO RETURN THROUGH ANOTHER CHOSEN ONE LIKE YOU..."

"...BUT A HOUSE OF ASSASSINS SLEW MY LOVE BEFORE MY ARMY WAS ASSEMBLED."

AHH! BUT NOW MY ARMY IS COMPLETE! AND WITH YOUR DEVOTION, MY POWER WILL BE CLOTHED IN FLESH YET AGAIN!

AND NOT EVEN THE RETURN OF THE VILE ASSASSIN TRIBE BEHIND YOU CAN STOP ME!

N-NO!!
HOW?!?
HOW DID YOU--?!

WE DO INDEED REMEMBER YOUR FOUL AMBITION, ANAT. THE MEMORY OF THE HOUSE OF SINANJU IS LONG...

...AND DETERMINED AS ALWAYS TO BANISH YOU FOREVER.
STAY AWAY FROM HER, YOU FREAK!

FLEE THIS PLACE, ROBERT...
YOU CANNOT FIGHT HIM THIS WAY...
THEN WHAT CAN--?

UNH!
SKEEEE!

RUN...!

I WISH THEY'D GET ON WITH IT.

MY FRIENDS! HEAR ME!
HEY, HOW ABOUT THAT?

IN YOUR MIDST IS THE EVIL ASSASSIN CULT! ONLY THE BIG DOG IN YOU CAN DETECT THEM!

GIVE IN TO IT SO YOU CAN DESTROY YOUR ENEMY! ONLY THEN WILL YOU BE TRULY FREE!
?

THESE ARE THOSE DIRECTLY RESPONSIBLE FOR THE HARDSHIPS YOU'VE ENDURED!
UH OH.

KILL THEM!!
NOW!!

FLEE, ROBERT...
LOOK...
I DON'T WANT TO HURT YOU KIDS...

YOU'D BETTER KNOCK IT OFF BEFORE I GET PISSED!

I CAN DODGE ALL DAY, BUT I DON'T HAVE TIME TO PLAY WITH YOU!
STOP IT!

REMO!!!
KINDA BUSY!!

WHOA!

BAM!!
THAT WAS FUN!
YOU HAVEN'T CARRIED ME IN A WHILE, HUH?

SILENCE!
I MUST INSTRUCT YOU IN THE TRUE NATURE OF THE THREAT!

IT WAS DURING THE TIME OF MASTER KIM...

ANOTHER KIM? OR IS THIS THE ONE WHO ALMOST MARRIED THE MONGOL CHICK?
NO.
THAT WAS THE FATHER OF VIMU, THE DISGRACED.

THEN YOU MEAN THE KIM WHO ONLY TOOK DIAMONDS AS PAYMENT?
NO.
HE DIED AS A YOUNG MASTER, KILLED BY A WEREWOLF.

THEN YOU MUST MEAN THE ONE WHO CARRIED THE WATER SKIN ON THE TIP OF HIS STAFF...
NO.
THAT WAS THE SON OF TIDI, SECURER OF THE HINDI ACCOUNTS.

THEN IT'S JUST GOT TO BE THE KIM WHO INVENTED THE SANDWICH ATTACK!
NO.
THAT WAS THE SON OF JOPKI.

KIM HAS ALWAYS BEEN A POPULAR NAME AMONG MY PEOPLE.
NO KIDDING?

NOW ATTEND!
MASTER KIM WAS KNOWN AS THE WANDERER.

"SO CALLED BECAUSE THERE WAS LITTLE WORK. THE MASTER WOULD WANDER TO DISTANT KINGDOMS OFFERING THE SERVICES OF SUPERIOR ASSASSINATION AT A DISCOUNT."

OBVIOUSLY THOSE DAYS WERE
ERY SAD."
"OH, OBVIOUSLY."
AFTER ONE PARTICULAR DAY
F WANDERING, KIM STOPPED TO REFRESH HIMSELF AT A TEMPLE."

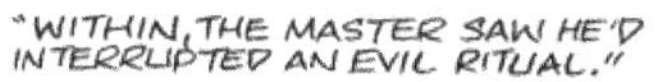
"WITHIN, THE MASTER SAW HE'D INTERRUPTED AN EVIL RITUAL."

"THE PRIESTS WERE ATTEMPTING TO SUMMON A LONG BANISHED WAR GODDESS FROM THE VOID...

THE ESSENCE OF ANAT, MISTRESS OF THE SKY,
NHABITED AN IDOL FASHIONED FROM PORRIDGE
THAT THEY FED TO HER CHOSEN ONE."

"ONCE AGAIN POSSESSED OF A BODY OF HER OWN, ANAT SOUGHT TO MAKE HER VICTORY COMPLETE BY RAISING UP A NEW ARMY, MAKING HER VIRTUALLY INVINCIBLE."

BUT FORTUNATELY, THE MASTER OF SINANJU FELL UPON HER BEFORE THIS COULD HAPPEN, THUS SAVING THE WORLD FROM THE FOUL DARK GOD.

WELL, IT **SOUNDS** LIKE ALL WE HAVE TO DO IS SMASH THE IDOL SO SHE CAN'T SHOW UP AND RAISE HER ARMY.
PIECE 'O CAKE!

SHE ALREADY **HAS** HER ARMY.
OBSERVE POWERS' **LEGIONS** OF FOLLOWERS.

OUR TASK IS TO PREVENT HER FROM INHABITING THE BODY OF HER NEW CHOSEN ONE.
YEAH?

THAT SOUNDS LIKE A JOB FOR THE DESTROYER!

GOOD!
I'VE BEEN WANTING TO SPLIT HIS SKULL ALL DAY!

EAT ME, ROBERT...
PARDON?

YOU MUST **CONSUME** THIS EFFIGY...
TAKE IT **INTO** YOU...

ONLY **THEN** MAY I WALK THE EARTH... AND WITH MY ARMY AT MY SIDE, NOT EVEN THE HOUSE OF SINANJU CAN STOP ME...
EAT...

EAT AND I WILL RE-FASHION YOUR FLESH SO THAT IT WILL SERVE MY CAUSE MORE EFFECTIVELY...
BUT...
BUT WHAT ABOUT **ME**?!

YOU WILL SERVE YOUR **GODDESS**... YOU CANNOT HOPE TO SURVIVE THE COMING BATTLE WITH SINANJU, ROBERT...
YOU WILL DIE IN **ANY** EVENT...

NOW **EAT!** TIME GROWS SHORT! I AM EAGER TO CLOTHE MYSELF IN FLESH!

SMASH

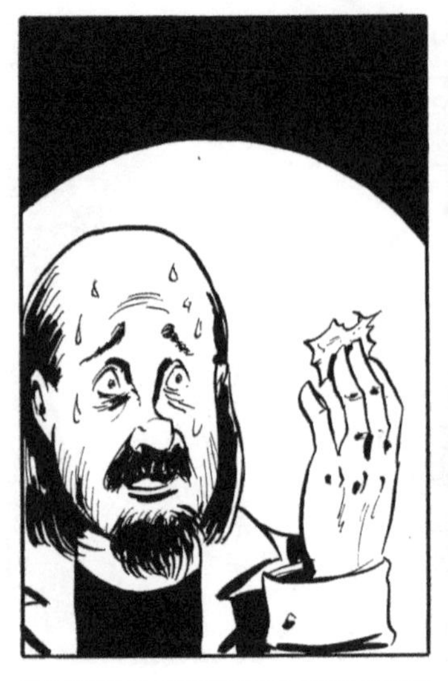

KKKKH!!

GRMMM!!
GRMH!!
KKK!!

PANT PANT PANT
PANT PANT

KRAAAAH!!
GRAAH!!
GRMM!!

WHAT THE HELL IS THAT HORRIBLE SOUND?
IT IS THE SOUND OF JAGGED METAL RIPPING THROUGH SOFT, WET FLESH.

STORAGE
EMPLOYEES ONLY
QUICKLY!
THIS WAY!

BAM!
STORAGE
NO!!
KKKKKKK...!
YOU ARE TOO LATE, FOOLS!

BEHOLD!!
THE RETURN OF ANAT!! MOTHER OF THE GODS!!

COME TO ME, MY SOLDIERS! MY BIG DOGS!
MAKE MY POWER COMPLETE!

FROM ALL ACROSS THE COUNTRY, SEEDS PLANTED BY THE WORDS OF THE LATE ROBERT POWERS AWAKEN INTO THE MINDS OF UNHOLY WARRIORS.

OF COURSE, THE SOLDIERS CLOSEST TO ANAT ARE THE BIGGEST THREAT...
KILL!
KILL!
KILL SINANJU!
KILL!
KILL!
KILL!
KILL SINANJU!
...THE SOUND OF THEIR FOOTFALLS THUNDERING TOWARD REMO AND CHIUN ARE DEAFENING.

NO!
STAY BACK!!

REMO!
REMEMBER THE LESSON OF KIM!
RIGHT!

WAIT A MINUTE...
WASN'T THE LESSON "IF SHE GETS A BODY WE'RE SCREWED?"
COME TO **ME**, PRETTY MORTAL.
LONG HAS IT BEEN SINCE I'VE KNOWN FLESHLY PLEASURE!

GIVE US A COUPLING BEFORE YOU ARE STAMPED INTO A BLOODY MUCK!
MMMM... **SEXY**.
WELL, SINCE YOU PUT IT **THAT** WAY...

...COME TO DADDY.

THUP THUP THUP THUP
THUP THUP

GARRRRH!!
WHAT?
THAT'S FOREPLAY.

RARRRH!!!
HEY, CALM DOWN, BABY.

THUP THUP
THUP THUP
THUP

SKREEE!
UH!

REMO, YOU DON'T HAVE TO FIGHT HER WITH A FINGER!
YOU'VE ALREA FAILED THAT LESSON!

FIGHT NORMAL!
OH.
WHY DIDN'T YOU SAY SO?

ARRRH!!

NOOOOOOOOOOOOO!

S ANAT'S ESSENCE IS
ELEASED FROM HER FLESHY
RMOR...
...THE MINDS OF HER SOLDIERS ARE RETURNED TO THEIR OWNERS.

FEARFUL THAT THE TWITCHING PIECES OF MEAT ARE TRYING TO RECONSTITUTE...

...THE TWO MASTERS OF SINANJU WORK TO DESTROY HER UTTERLY, UNAWARE THAT HER ESSENCE HAS ALREADY ESCAPED...

.AND QUICKLY WORKS TO
OSSESS NEW OBJECTS
ORTHY ENOUGH FOR HER
ORSHIP.

WELL! ALL IN A DAY'S WORK! PIECE 'O CAKE.
NATURALLY, YOU'VE FAILED TO OBSERVE THAT IT WAS I BURDENED WITH ALL OF THE REAL WORK.
TYPICAL.

CHANTILLY, VIRGINIA.
NINE YEARS LATER...
WESTFIELD HIGH SCHOOL

SETTLE DOWN NOW, CLASS. TAKE YOUR SEATS.
PLEASE TURN TO PAGE H EIGHTEEN.

LOOK AT HIM. HE'S SO STUPID.
SH! THE TEACHER IS LOOKING.

HEY, CHO. WHY ARE YOU SO STUPID?
SHUT UP!

HERE'S A DOLLAR, CHO. SAY SOMETHING STUPID.
THE NIHILIST RECIPES

GIGGLE
LEAVE HIM ALONE, BILLY.
THE NIHILIST RECIPES
S.H. CHO

FOR WHAT?
WHAT'S HE GOING TO DO?
THE NIHILIST RECIPES
S.H. CHO
END

中

中

SCROLLS OF SINANJU:

THE SUNSOURCE

STORY AND ART BY M. RASHEED
BASED ON CHARACTERS CREATED BY WARREN MURPHY AND RICHARD SAPIR

AS YOU KNOW FROM MY PREVIOUS SCROLL ENTRIES, I HAVE TAKEN TO THE HABIT OF CLIMBING TO THE TOP OF KOREA'S HIGHEST MOUNTAIN, TO MEDITATE WITHIN A SMALL CAVE I FOUND THERE.

THIS DAY IN QUESTION WAS NO EXCEPTION, AS BEFORE I FORBAD THE ARMY OF SUSPICIOUS NIGHT TIGERS TO FOLLOW, AMIDST MUCH GRUMBLING.

EAGER TO ESCAPE FROM THE DRUDGERY OF THE DAY, I DID NOT EVEN BECOME EXASPERATED AT THE SOUNDS OF A FEW OF THE SENIORS CLIMBING UP ANY WAY.

GROWING INCREASINGLY INSUBORDI ATE AS THEY CONTINUED TO JOCKE FOR POSITION AS TO WHO WOULD BE NEXT IN LINE FOR THE MASTE HOOD, I DID NOT CARE AS LONG AS THEY DID NOT TALK TO ME.
5

MY MEDITATION HAD GROWN QUITE INTERESTING, AS I EXPERIMENTED WITH A SPECIAL BREATHING TECHNIQUE LEARNED BY MASTER WO-TI DURING HIS MANY DECADES IN EGYPT. IN THE LAST FEW SESSIONS IT APPEARED AS IF MY FIELD OF VISION EXPANDED EVEN THOUGH I SAW ONLY TOTAL DARKNESS, AND I VERY MUCH WISHED TO DUPLICATE THE EFFECT.

BUT THIS TIME...

...I SAW SOMETHING...

...FAR MORE REMARKABLE THAN I HAD ANTICIPATED!
57

WANG.
OH, MY...!
WHO ARE YOU?

THAT IS NOT IMPORTANT. WHAT IS IMPORTANT IS THAT YOU HEED ME...

...FOR I HAVE MUCH TO TEACH, AN
YOU HAVE MUCH TO LEARN.

THE STRANGE SPIRIT BEING WHO WAS ME, YET NOT ME, SEEMED TO TALK FOR DAYS.

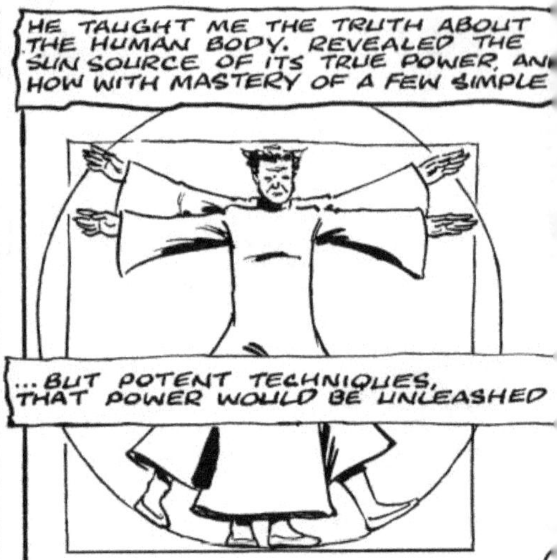
HE TAUGHT ME THE TRUTH ABOUT THE HUMAN BODY. REVEALED THE SUN SOURCE OF ITS TRUE POWER, AN
HOW WITH MASTERY OF A FEW SIMPLE
...BUT POTENT TECHNIQUES, THAT POWER WOULD BE UNLEASHED

WHEN I RECOVERED FROM MY TRANCE, THE SUN HAD NOT MOVED A DOT FROM ITS POSITION, BUT MUCH HAD CHANGED.

N SECONDS I FELLED THEM ALL... CUTTING A SWATHE OF DEATH THROUGH HESE WARRIORS WITHOUT PEER AS IF THEY WERE DEFENSELESS CHILDREN!

THEIR SERVICES WILL NO LONGER BE NEEDED. THE SUN SOURCE OF SINANJU MUST BE PROTECTED.
ONLY A SINGLE APPRENTICE AT A TIME WILL BE TRAINED IN THE TECHNIQUES. TOMORROW I WILL GO OUT AND INTRODUCE THE TRUE SINANJU TO THE KINGS OF THE WORLD.
SO SAYS WANG THE GREAT!
END

ABOUT
THE
AUTHOR

M. Rasheed is a permanent vendor at the North Carolina State Fairgrounds and popularly known for his Cartoon Portraits, which enable lucky patrons to pose with their favorite cartoon characters and celebrities in the artist's fun/friendly drawing style.

Highly prolific, M. Rasheed is also the cartoonist behind the *Monsters 101* graphic novel series, *Wild Hunt*, and many fascinating web stories, which includes a YouTube channel featuring original Adobe Flash animated shorts.

He received his B.F.A. from the College of Creative Studies in Detroit, Michigan and is proud to admit that he was one of the "Dogs of 1-D" from the Joe Kubert School of Cartoon and Graphic Art, Inc.

Additional copies of this book
and other titles from
Second Sight Graphix
are available for ordering
at www.mrasheed.com,
and www.amazon.com.
You may also use the
handy coupon on the
following page to order
by mail.

For more info about
our titles please
visit our website!

http://www.mrasheed.com

o, you would like to be one of the *Shemesu Heru*, the Followers of Second Sight?
Then you'd better start collecting more books from Second Sight Graphix!

Here are a few more titles you'll enjoy:

_____Tales of Sinanju: The Destroyer, book two
"End Date" $10.00

_____Tales of Sinanju: The Destroyer, book three
"Free Fall" $10.00

_____Tales of Sinanju: The Destroyer, book four
"Focal Point" $10.00

_____Tales of Sinanju: The Destroyer, book five
"Death Dance" $10.00

_____Tales of Sinanju: The Destroyer, book six
"Eviction Notice" $10.00

____ Monsters 101, book one
"From Bully to Monster" $15.00

Second Sight Graphix

Second Sight Graphix Dept. OPS
7413 Six Forks Road, Suite 207, Raleigh NC 27615-4190

Please send me the books I have checked above. I am enclosing $________________.
I understand this will include the postage, and I am sending a bank cashiers check or money order ONLY (no cash).
I also understand I am to allow 6-8 weeks for delivery.

NAME______________________________________

ADDRESS____________________________________

CITY______________ **STATE**________ **ZIP**____________

Treat Yourself to a **MONSTROUS** Binge Reac

This ten-title, 1500-page masterpiece of science fantasy is a great way to spend a long weekend! From the author of the *Tales of Sinanju: The Destroyer* graphic novels, *Monsters 101* is full of the super-fun you've come to expect from the pen of cartoonist M. Rasheed. For more info: www.mrasheed.co

Miracle Happens
FROM BRUCE DWAYNE
VARIANT COVER ART BY
ALE GARZA
(BATGIRL, TEEN TITANS, DEADPOOL)
FRENZIED FU FIGHTING!
MIRACLE MARTIAL MODEL
CLOUD EAGLE ENTERTAINMENT
WWW.FACEBOOK.COM/CLOUDEAGLES WWW.CLOUDEAGLE.COM
Miracle & Cloud Eagle (C) 2013 Cloud Eagle Entertainment

CPSIA information can be obtained
at www.ICGtesting.com
Printed in the USA
BVHW030214160419
545635BV00002B/84/P